A.C.T. I
(Revised)

AFFECTIVE COGNITIVE THINKING

STRATEGIES FOR THE GIFTED

Revised by

Nathan Levy and Scott Hobson

Nathan Levy

Written by: Lynne A. Blymire, Thomas L. Brunner, Clarence J. Jones

Nathan Levy Books, LLC
18 Moorland Blvd.
Monroe Township, NJ 08831
Phone: 732-605-1643
FAX: 732-656-7822
www.storieswithholes.com

A.C.T. I

Thinking Strategies
For The Gifted

A.C.T. I is a workbook of activities designed for Gifted Students based on cognitive thinking and affective process skills. Our position is that activities for gifted children must stress advanced conceptualization and the higher level thinking skills of interpretation, translation, application, analysis, synthesis, and evaluation. These cognitive thinking skills and affective process skills offer opportunities for original and elaborative thinking. Students will have to take risks by defending their own ideas or by taking guesses. They may seek alternatives to complex problems and must be willing to follow hunches, wonder, or play with ideas. Students will enjoy the opportunity to visualize, reach out, and dream about things that have never happened. These activities and thought questions urge new and unique combinations of existing elements to produce original products.

The pages of this workbook may be completed in any order. You will find that many of the activities can be easily integrated with content from your curriculum. Some activities may further explore personal or hobby interests. It will be helpful for you to use the record-keeping charts by dating when each lesson is begun. Additional work pages have been added to complete many of the activities. Encourage students to follow the ten guidelines given in the STUDENT'S SECTION, and always be ready for a new product that you did not expect or predict!

Table of Contents

SCIENCE – LIVING THINGS   111

SCIENCE – THE EARTH AND BEYOND   135

SCIENCE – MACHINES, IDEAS AND INVENTIONS   158

This book has been designed to offer experiences in thinking beyond the usual things expected in school. It is not a basic educational text, but is a collection of exercises written to stretch your mind and challenge your basic factual understanding.

You may begin anywhere in the book and work in any order. You may decide to do activities that are related to topics presented by your teacher. Perhaps your activity decision will follow readings and interests you have developed on your own. These activities will lead you into thinking which involves deeper search and effort.

To get the fullest benefit from your book, you will need to think critically and creatively.

Follow These Guidelines:

1. Read and learn as much about the topic as you can before working in your book.
2. Keep an open mind.
3. Think in as many ways as you possibly can to arrive at decisions.
4. When you are challenged by a puzzling question, think deeply about it.
5. Try to think of many ideas.
6. Plan your work carefully.
7. In your drawings and explanations, be original and take time to answer with exact, complete thoughts.
8. Work neatly and carefully!
9. When you are stuck for ideas, do not give up! Try to look at the problem in a new or different way.
10. TAKE PRIDE IN YOUR WORK!

Use this book as often as you have time. Use separate sheets of paper to complete your activities. When you are finished, you will have a deeper awareness and understanding of your world. Perhaps you will soon agree that deep thinking is a challenge and great fun!

GOOD THINKING TO YOU!

LANGUAGE ARTS

Activities	Date Begun	Teacher's Initials

NURSERY RHYMES

1. Humpty Dumpty
2. Baa, Baa Black Sheep
3. Hickory Dickory Dock
4. Little Miss Muffet
5. Old Mother Hubbard
6. The Old Woman in a Shoe
7. Hey Diddle Diddle
8. This Little Pig Went to Market
9. Georgie Porgie

FAIRY TALES

10. Hansel and Gretel
11. Little Red Riding Hood
12. Goldilocks and the 3 Bears
13. Cinderella
14. The Three Little Pigs
15. Rumpelstiltskin
16. The Pied Piper of Hamlin

SPECIAL DAYS AND HOLIDAYS

17. Thanksgiving
18. Halloween
19. Christmas
20. Arbor Day

Activities	Date Begun	Teacher's Initials

SELECTED LITERATURE ACTIVITIES

23. Folktales

24. Mythology

25. American Legendary Heroes

26. Magazines

27. What Do Words Really Say?

28. Historical Readings

29. Suggestions for Book Reports

QUESTIONS OF MY OWN

Humpty Dumpty

Why did Humpty Dumpty fall off the wall?

Suggest ways that the King's soldiers could have put Humpty Dumpty together again.

    1.

    2.

    3.

    4.

    5.

Draw a picture of Humpty Dumpty put "back together again."

What could you do with a broken Humpty Dumpty?

    1.

    2.

    3.

How would this story be different if Humpty Dumpty had been sitting on a bridge over water?

Baa, Baa Black Sheep

What color was the sheep's wool?

How heavy is a bag of wool?

Why do you think so?

What would you do with a bag of wool?

Wool is a fabric used to make cloth. List clothing made from wool.

1.   5.

2.   6.

3.   7.

4.   8.

If a sheep could talk to you, what would he say after his wool had been sheared? Write the conversation you would have.

Hickory Dickory Dock

Why did the mouse run up the clock?

**Do you think the clock was striking one during the afternoon
or one during the night? Explain your answer.**

**Draw a picture showing the clock striking one and what may have
been happening at the same time.**

Little Miss Muffet

Why did Little Miss Muffet run away?

Where did Little Miss Muffet go?

How would this story be different if a kitten sat down beside Miss Muffet?

Read about spiders. Explain how spiders are helpful to people.

Draw a picture to show what you would do if a spider sat down beside you.

Old Mother Hubbard

How old is Old Mother Hubbard?

What kind of dog did
Mother Hubbard own?

Tell why Mother Hubbard's
cupboard might have been bare.

How would this story have been
different if Mother Hubbard had
been getting food for a parakeet?

What animal is best as a household pet? Tell why you think so.

List things you have to do to care for a pet.

1.   4.

2.   5.

3.   6.

The Old Woman in a Shoe

How many children is "so many" children?

Where did all of those children come from?

Do you think the old woman loved the children? Why or why not?

Draw the inside of a "shoe house."
Label each room. Include things like furniture, color, etc.

Hey Diddle Diddle

What tune would a cat play on a fiddle?

How could a cow get into outer space?

What problems would a cow have in outer space?

1.   4.

2.   5.

3.   6.

How would the cow return to her barnyard?

Why was the little dog laughing? Suggest three possible reasons.

1.

2.

3.

Where did the dish and the spoon go?

This Little Pig Went to Market

Suggest things the first little pig may buy at the market.

What other foods did the third little pig eat with his roast beef? Draw a picture to show his dinner plate.

Why would a little pig cry? Explain your ideas.

Suggest games little pigs might play.

1.   4.

2.   5.

3.   6.

How would this story have been different if the "Big, Bad Wolf" had been close by?

Why did the little girls cry?

In your opinion, what would Georgie Porgie have done if the little girls had kissed him?

What does a kiss really tell you?

What did the little boys in Georgie's neighborhood think of Georgie's behavior?

Was Georgie Porgie a good boy or a bad boy? Why do you think so?

How would you feel if you were kissed by a classmate at school? Draw your expression on one of these faces.

Hansel and Gretel

Name some cookies and candies the old witch may have used to build her house.

1.   6.

2.   7.

3.   8.

4.   9.

5.   10.

What kind of weather would be necessary if houses were made of candy and cookies?

What problems would we have if homes could be eaten?

Draw a picture of the gingerbread house. Color it.

Little Red Riding Hood

Suggest food that Little Red Riding Hood may have carried in her basket.

1.   5.

2.   6.

3.   7.

4.   8.

Draw a picture of the bouquet of flowers that Little Red Riding Hood collected while in the meadow.

Suggest kinds of flowers she may have picked.

How would this story have changed if Little Red Riding Hood had worn blue or yellow?

On another sheet of paper, draw a map to show the route Little Red Riding Hood took to get to Grandmother's house. Include places, things, and people along the way.

Goldilocks and the Three Bears

Draw a picture of the three bears' home.
Show the rooms described in the story.

Was Goldilocks a good girl or a bad girl? Explain your answer.

What lesson did Goldilocks learn from her adventure?

List "rules of etiquette" that Goldilocks did not follow.

1.

2.

3.

4.

Cinderella

List the parts of the story that could have happened.

1.   5.

2.   6.

3.   7.

4.

List the parts of the story that could not have happened.

1.   5.

2.   6.

3.   7.

4.

If you could meet your "Fairy Godmother", what would you ask her to do?

Imagine that you can add more to the ending of this story. How would Cinderella have changed in one year? Write your ideas.

The Three Little Pigs

Suggest methods of assembling a house made of straw.

1.   3.

2.   4.

**Describe the weather conditions you would
need to live in a house constructed of straw.**

**In your opinion, was the wolf really bad?
Why or why not?**

Suggest ways the wolf earned the title of "Big, Bad Wolf."

1.   4.

2.   5.

3.   6.

**Read all about winds, especially about measuring the speed of wind.
In your estimation, how strong a wind would the wolf have blown to
knock down a house made of straw?**

How strong would the wind need to be to blow over a house made of sticks?

Rumpelstiltskin

Draw a picture that shows the gold that the "little man" spun from the straw.

Was Rumpelstiltskin a good man or a bad man? Why do you think so?

Think of some other unusual names Rumpelstiltskin could have used.

1.   4.

2.   5.

3.   6.

The Pied Piper of Hamlin

Tell how the parents felt when their children disappeared.

What did the children do in the mountain?
Draw a picture to show your ideas.

Was the Pied Piper a good or bad person? Explain your thinking.

Suggest another way this story could have ended.
Draw a picture to show your ending.

LANGUAGE ARTS: Special Days and Holidays

In your opinion, why did the Native Americans help the Pilgrims?

Explain how you feel in a new situation. Include your thoughts and feelings.

If you had been a Pilgrim child, what job would you have done on the settlement?

Draw a picture to show the way you helped the settlement.

On another paper, list the words you have learned about Pilgrims, Native Americans, and the first Thanksgiving. Then on the next page, make a hidden word puzzle by writing your words on the grid going up, down, forward, backward, or diagonally. Add other letters to the empty spaces left on your grid. Share your puzzle with your teacher and classmates.

Thanksgiving

Halloween

Invent a new "monster" to add to our existing creatures of fright. Give it a name and explain how it frightens people. Draw it here.

Invent a method of protection against scary creatures in these areas.

WORDS

MECHANISMS

CONDITIONS

SPECIAL HUMAN ABILITIES

Christmas

Name and describe any toy or game you wish.

Illustrate Santa's workshop on the next page. Show the assembly line needed to make the toy or game you listed above.

Rename the reindeer. Choose a theme and be original.

1.

2.

3.

4.

5.

6.

7.

8.

9.

Devise a new sleigh for Santa. Consider space for toys, comfort for Santa, power to travel quickly and quietly, and a communication system to avoid problems with aircraft. Draw it here.

Santa's Workshop

Arbor Day

Read about Arbor Day celebrations across the United States.
List some states and when they celebrate Arbor Day (see example).

1. Pennsylvania – last Friday in April

2.

3.

4.

5.

6.

7.

8.

9.

10.

11.

12.

13.

14.

15.

16.

17.

Do you see a relationship between the location of the states you listed above and when they celebrate Arbor Day? Is there a pattern among the states you have read about?

On the map of the United States, show patterns by coloring states with April celebrations yellow, May celebrations orange, and June celebrations red (or choose your own colors). Fill in the names of the states on the map.

On a sheet of graph paper, make a crossword puzzle of your own. Write clear clues for answers going across and down. Watch your numbers and spellings. Suggestions for your word list may be parts of trees, kinds of trees, or products.

Map of United States

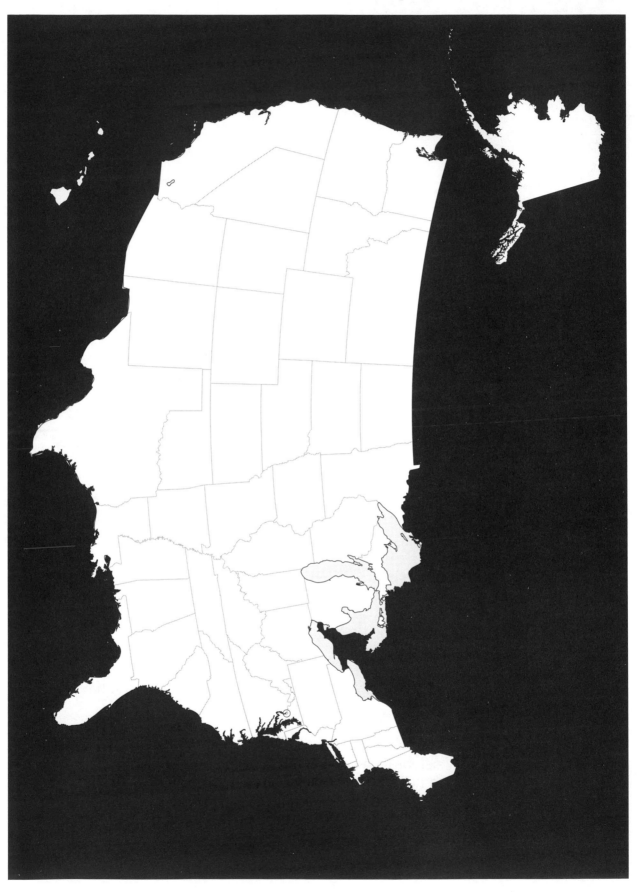

Folktales

Read folktales from America and another country of your choice.

List similarities you find in your selections.

    1.

    2.

    3.

    4.

    5.

    6.

Prepare a speech to relate the main ideas of one tale from each of your countries. Begin by outlining the main ideas and events, then point out the similarities. Conclude with your own judgment about each story or tale.

Mythology

Make a chart or diagram showing the relationships of the gods and goddesses in any Greek, Roman, or Norse mythology (choose one).

Research and read the end of "Pandora." According to some versions of the mythology, Zeus created Pandora. If like Pandora you had a box, list the blessings you would put in it. Would you open the box? If yes, when and what would you do?

American Legendary Heroes

Compile a list of remarkable skills and amazing feats of the different American legendary heroes.

	HERO TITLE/NAME	AMAZING FEAT OR REMARKABLE SKILLS
1.		
2.		
3.		
4.		
5.		
6.		
7.		
8.		

Choose one legendary hero. Explain why you believe American people needed a legendary hero like this.

Magazines

Read at least three magazines from this suggested group.
List the magazines you have read.

CRICKET	BOYS' LIFE
WORLD	SPORTS ILLUSTRATED
RANGER RICK	ODYSSEY
HIGHLIGHTS	HUMPTY DUMPTY
OWL	KID CRAFTS

1.

2.

3.

Record similarities in theme/idea among the magazines you listed.

1.

2.

3.

4.

5.

Describe the kinds of writings you saw in each magazine.

Describe the illustrations or photographs in each.

Which magazine on the list is your favorite? Why?

My Magazine

Imagine designing a magazine for children. List areas of content and writing styles your staff would have to consider to make and publish your magazine.

	AREAS OF CONTENT	STYLES OF WRITING
1.		
2.		
3.		
4.		
5.		

Make a Table of Contents for the first issue of your magazine.

What would you name your magazine?

On the next page, illustrate the cover of your first issue.

What Do Words Really Say?

Read *The King Who Reigned, Chocolate Mousse for Dinner,* **or any of the books about Amelia Bedelia. Illustrate the phrases below.**

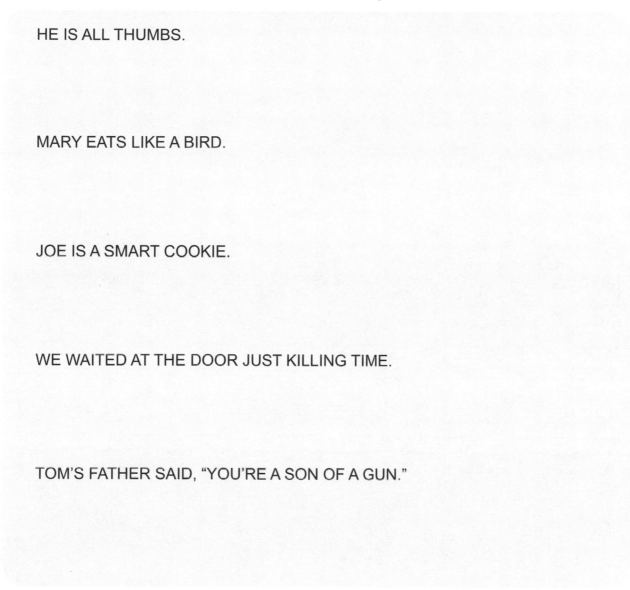

HE IS ALL THUMBS.

MARY EATS LIKE A BIRD.

JOE IS A SMART COOKIE.

WE WAITED AT THE DOOR JUST KILLING TIME.

TOM'S FATHER SAID, "YOU'RE A SON OF A GUN."

Evaluate the effect of saying, "You're a smart cookie" instead of "You are a smart little girl." Consider which phrase may be most effective and explain why you think so.

On the next page, write some phrases of your own. Illustrate any that you wish.

Phrases

Historical Readings

Read three books on a similar topic written by different authors. Choose one of these topics:

1. Factual books of history

2. Biographies of the same person

3. Historical fiction books on the same period of time

Compare and contrast the following areas:

Style of telling the story

1.

2.

3.

Illustrations

1.

2.

3.

Vocabulary

1.

2.

3.

Accuracy or authenticity

1.

2.

3.

Appeal to you as the reader

1.

2.

3.

Suggestions for Book Reports
Considerations Based on Higher-level Thought

1. Is the setting authentic? Explain your ideas.

2. Do the characters represent realistic human personalities? Compare a scene in the book to a real-life situation to illustrate realism in personality development.

3. Is the dialogue between characters believable or natural? Choose a passage from your reading to show your opinion on this question.

4. Does the book portray living and life as you know it? Compare or contrast excerpts to explain your answer.

Suggested Activities for Book Reports
Considerations Based on Higher-level Thought

5. With which character did you most identify? Explain why.

6. If this story takes place during a different period of time, are you, the reader, made aware of that time? List several examples from your reading that help the reader identify the period of time.

Questions of My Own

As you are thinking, you may design a deep thought question of your own. Record the lesson you were working on and the date of your work. Write each question clearly and neatly.

Lesson #   Date   My Questions

_____   _____   _____

_____   _____   _____

_____   _____   _____

_____   _____   _____

_____   _____   _____

_____   _____   _____

_____   _____   _____

_____   _____   _____

_____   _____   _____

_____   _____   _____

_____   _____   _____

_____   _____   _____

SOCIAL STUDIES

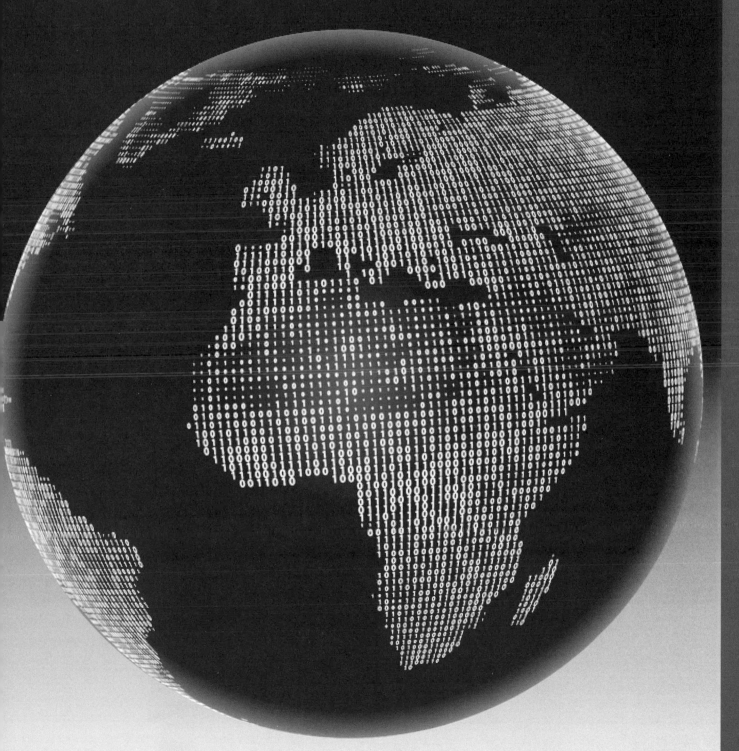

Activities	Date Begun	Teacher's Initials
1. Human Qualities		
2. Anxiety		
3. Fears and Phobias		
4. Frustration		
5. Fun		
6. Heroes		
7. Athletic Competitions		
8. Secrets		
9. Young and Old		
10. New Solutions for		
11. What If?		
12. What If? – The Common Cold		
13. What If? – A New Home		
14. Robot Friend		
15. The World of the Future		
16. Transportation for the Future		
17. Change		
18. Knights		
19. Pioneers		
20. Boys and Girls Today		
21. "Spare the Rod,		
QUESTIONS OF MY OWN		

Human Qualities

You have met many people. Each person possesses qualities which may appeal to some people and not to others. In your opinion, which quality is the most valuable to a person? Why?

Which personality trait is of most benefit to success in friendship? Explain your thinking.

Which personality trait is most beneficial to success in school? Explain your answer.

Describe the traits you consider to be most harmful to humankind.

1.   6.
2.   7.
3.   8.
4.   9.
5.   10.

In your judgment, which trait is the MOST harmful from your list above? Tell why you feel this way.

Anxiety

Describe your feelings when you are in a new situation. Some examples of such a situation may be joining a new club, attending a camp during the summer, or joining a sports team.

Explain how you help yourself control your anxiety.

Fears and Phobias

Why do people show fear?

Talk to five children that are about your age, five children older than you, and five adults. Ask each person what he fears. List their fears in the appropriate column below.

	CHILDREN MY AGE	OLDER CHILDREN	ADULTS
1.			
2.			
3.			
4.			
5.			

Compare these lists. Circle any fears that show up in all age groups. Suggest reasons why this may be true.

Frustration

Here is a man who will be late for work because he is stuck in heavy traffic. What is he thinking? Draw small illustrations or list the thoughts that may be going through his mind.

Fun

Think of happy times in your life when you were having fun. What makes something FUN? List things that are fun for you.

1.

2.

3.

4.

5.

6.

7.

8.

Now ask other people what is fun for them. Record their responses.

1.

2.

3.

4.

5.

6.

7.

8.

What conclusions can you make about having fun? Is there just one single characteristic of fun?

With your old and new ideas about fun, create a FUN MACHINE. Draw your machine on the following page. Label the different parts of the machine, color it, and give it a name. Later, you may want to copy your Fun Machine onto poster board or craft paper.

My Fun Machine

Heroes

Study the meaning of the word "hero."

Choose a hero in any area of interest for you. For example: a hero in medicine, government, politics, war, etc.

Describe your hero's qualities that you admire most.

In what way was your hero's childhood like yours?

How is your childhood different?

Athletic Competitions

Roger Federer won the Tennis Tournament at Wimbledon in 2003, 2004, 2005, 2006, 2007 but lost in 2008. He won again in 2009 and then lost in 2010.

Suggest reasons why a superstar tennis player, or an athlete in any sport, may not win every time.

1.
2.
3.
4.
5.
6.

Choose two interesting people in sports. Read all you can about each athlete. Compare their families. Notice how each one trained. Are there any generalizations you can infer from your reading?

Compile a list of "Do's" and "Don'ts" for an athlete in training.

1.
2.
3.
4.
5.
6.
7.

Secrets

Occasionally the newspaper tells of unfortunate events about children.

Explain why a child might keep secrets from adults.

Explain why a child might keep a secret from friends.

Suggest ways to eliminate this problem for a child who has no one to tell about his or her problems.

1.

2.

3.

4.

5.

Write a story describing the emotional tension of both the parents and the frightened child. Include a workable solution for this rightly capable, but frightened child.

Optional: Read the book <u>Rachel Mason Hears the Sound</u> by Cindy Lovell, published by Nathan Levy Books, LLC.

Young and Old

What are some of the problems confronting young people? Begin first by defining "young": Birth to age _____ .

Now list problems facing young people.

1.	5.
2.	6.
3.	7.
4.	8.

How old is "old"? Describe your idea of old with a number or a physical condition: _____ .

Now list problems facing old people.

1.	5.
2.	6.
3.	7.
4.	8.

Look over both lists. Circle any problems that people face whether they are young or old. Suggest reasons for this.

Choose one problem and suggest ways to handle the problem or perhaps to eliminate it.

New Solutions for Old Problems

Here are some problems older people face. Can you suggest solutions for each problem? Write your ideas in the space after each problem.

1. Illness or poor health

2. High medical expenses

3. Feeling lonely

4. Losing loved ones

5. Poor self-esteem (feeling useless to society)

6. Compulsory (forced) retirement

7. Cannot move quickly or easily

Suggest another problem and its solution.

What If?

People (males and females) no longer have hair on their heads. How would this change styles? How would people dress differently in summer? In winter?

What if people no longer had ears?
How would this change fashion?

What else would be different?

What If? – The Common Cold

Can you predict how life would be different if the common cold were a fatal disease? In your explanation, consider methods of dress, activity limitations, medicines, scientific improvement emphasis, and attitudes of health care.

What If? – A New Home

Imagine that you could live in any country, with any climate, and any people you wish...

Draw a plan of your new home.

Draw a physical map of your neighborhood. Show the position of your home in relation to other homes and geographic features.

Describe the people you would live with, including the qualities you consider important for your new style of living.

Robot Friend

Design a robot to be your companion. List things you would want your robot to do for you and with you.

FOR ME   WITH ME

1.

2.

3.

4.

5.

6.

7.

8.

Of all the things your robot can do, what one thing is most important to you? Explain your choice.

On the next page, draw your robot friend. On your drawing, include labels and measurements, materials to be used, and special features.

Robot Friend

The World of the Future

Design a home for the future. Consider living quarters, leisure facilities, power sources, construction materials, etc. Use labels to explain your new home.

Transportation for the Future

Design transportation for the future. Your design may utilize water, land, or air space. Use measurement and labels when possible.

Change

"Civilizations change when they meet a new culture."
Explain this statement in your own words.

Relate an incident in history that shows this to be a true statement.

Can you also relate a historic event to prove this statement false?

In your opinion, could an old civilization offer any contributions to the new intruding culture? Explain your thinking.

List some ways each culture could contribute to or change the other group.

1.

2.

3.

4.

5.

6.

7.

Knights

Read all you can about the training of young boys, pages, and squires during the Middle Ages.

Outline the steps involved in the training of a boy for knighthood.

Illustrate a knight using his training in an adventurous situation.

Pioneers

Research the training of young boys during the early years of our country. Compile a list of skills necessary to live a comfortable existence as a pioneer.

1.
2.
3.
4.
5.
6.
7.
8.
9.
10.

Compare and contrast this training for young boys with that of the Middle Ages. Explain any similarities you find.

Boys and Girls Today

Consider activities both in and out of school that help teach skills to young people in our 21st century society. For example, think about scouting, 4-H, camps, gym class, language arts, etc.

Compile two lists.

Common Activities and Skills in the Middle Ages, Pioneer America, and 21st Century	New Skills Necessary ONLY in the 21st Century

"Spare the Rod, Spoil the Child"

List behaviors that you believe should be punished.

1.   5.
2.   6.
3.   7.
4.   8.

List various forms of punishment.

1.
2.
3.
4.
5.

Which punishment do you judge to be most effective?

Evaluate the effectiveness of physical punishment for wrong-doings.

In your own words, restate the quotation at the top of the page.

Do you believe this quotation to be true? Why or why not?

Questions of My Own

As you are thinking, you may design a deep thought question of your own. Record the lesson you were working on and the date of your work. Write each question clearly and neatly.

Lesson #	Date	My Questions
_____	_____	_____
_____	_____	_____
_____	_____	_____
_____	_____	_____
_____	_____	_____
_____	_____	_____
_____	_____	_____
_____	_____	_____
_____	_____	_____
_____	_____	_____
_____	_____	_____
_____	_____	_____

MATHEMATICS

Activities	Date Begun	Teacher's Initials
1. Numbers		
2. How Do You Measure Up?		
3. My Time Line		
4. "Take Your Medicine"		
5. "One" and More "One"		
6. "One" Again		
7. Try a Harder "One"		
8. Largest Cities		
9. Triangle Challenge		
10. Circles and Spirals		
11. Temperature		
12. Can You Find It?		
13. Number Pattern Designs		
14. Your Heart Rate		
15. Polygons		
16. Sides, Faces, Vertices & Edges		
17. Family Tree and Relatives		
18. Little		
19. Big		
20. Order		
21. Symmetry		
22. Perspective Drawing		
23. Tangrams		
24. Flow Charts		
25. Stock Exchange		
26. Coins		
QUESTIONS OF MY OWN		

Numbers

Numbers play an important role in our lives. Pretend that for a 24-hour period, all of the numbers have disappeared from the earth.

How would this affect your daily living? Consider:

1. Weighing yourself

2. Buying food

3. Using the phone

Offer alternative methods for each of the activities listed above.

1. Weighing yourself

2. Buying food

3. Using the phone

Make a list of the many differences there would be in your life if numbers did not exist.

1.

2.

3.

4.

5.

6.

7.

8.

9.

10.

How Do You Measure Up?

Stretch open your hand on another sheet of paper. Trace it. Measure from the top of the little finger to the tip of the thumb. Label the units.

Compare the length of your hand measurement to:

Length of foot

Length of arm

Length of face

Distance from knee to ankle

Distance from knee to hip

Are these statements true for your body? Record your measurements.

Twice around the thumb = once around the wrist?

Twice around the wrist = once around the neck?

Twice around the waist = your height?

Your height = your width? *

* Width indicates measurement of left arm to right arm in an outstretched position (arm span).

My Time Line

Make a time line of your life. Include the important things you have done or that have happened to you. Here are some ideas to consider.

Family Members   Vacation & Trips   Your Health

Famous Firsts   Friends   Special Accomplishments

Use the Time Line on this page to outline your life.

_____

BIRTH   1   2

_____

3   4   5

_____

6   7   8

"Take Your Medicine"

Use 15 objects to play this game.

You and your partner take turns by removing one or two objects in each turn. The person to pick up the last object is the loser. The loser has to take his medicine.

Is there a way to win every time?

Are there different numbers of objects to use in playing this game and still have the same results?

Can you make up another name for this game?

"One"

Write ten equations using both addition and subtraction in this pattern to equal one.

$a - (b + c) = 1$ Example: $10 - (8 + 1) = 1$

1.   6.

2.   7.

3.   8.

4.   9.

5.   10.

More "One"

Now write ten equations using both multiplication and subtraction in this pattern to equal one.

$a - (b \times c) = 1$ Example: $15 - (7 \times 2) = 1$

1.   6.

2.   7.

3   8.

4.   9.

5.   10.

"One" Again

Continue using subtraction and multiplication, but now use this pattern to make equations to equal one.

(__ x __) − (__ x __) = 1   **Example: (3 x 2) − (5 x 1) = 1**

1.

2.

3.

4.

5.

6.

7.

8.

9.

10.

Try a Harder "One"

Write ten more equations using the operations of subtraction and division in this pattern to equal one.

$$a - (b \div c) = 1 \qquad \text{Example: } 7 - (12 \div 2) = 1$$

1.　　　　　　　　　　　　　6.

2.　　　　　　　　　　　　　7.

3.　　　　　　　　　　　　　8.

4.　　　　　　　　　　　　　9.

5.　　　　　　　　　　　　　10.

Continue using subtraction and division using this new pattern to make equations that equal one.

$$(a \div b) - (c \div d) = 1 \qquad \text{Example: } (56 \div 8) - (42 \div 7) = 1$$

1.　　　　　　　　　　　　　6.

2.　　　　　　　　　　　　　7.

3.　　　　　　　　　　　　　8.

4.　　　　　　　　　　　　　9.

5.　　　　　　　　　　　　　10.

Largest Cities

Use an atlas or various sources to find the populations of the eight largest cities and eight largest countries. Record your data below.

	CITIES	COUNTRIES
1.		
2.		
3.		
4.		
5.		
6.		
7.		
8.		

Make graphs to show these large populations.

CITY   NUMBER IN POPULATION

COUNTRY

Largest Cities

Can you make any conclusions when comparing the largest cities and countries? List your conclusions.

1.

2.

3.

4.

5.

Refer to your atlas again.
List the largest countries by size or land mass.

1.   5.

2.   6.

3.   7.

4.   8.

Make a graph to show land mass or size of the country.

COUNTRY   SIZE

Compare the graphs for largest populations of countries and largest land mass. List any interesting similarities.

1.

2.

3.

Triangle Challenge

Draw an equilateral triangle with a side measurement of 3" (inches).

Draw a similar triangle below. Using your ruler to measure and make straight lines, further divide this large triangle into smaller equilateral triangles. How many can you make? _____

Color the second figure to create an interesting geometric design.

Triangle Challenge

Draw a large right triangle. Divide this triangle into smaller right triangles. How many can you make? _____

Now draw a large isosceles triangle. Divide the isosceles triangle into smaller isosceles triangles. How many can you make? _____

Circles and Spirals

Draw a series of concentric circles on the next page. Label the diameter of each circle in your arrangement.

Now draw a large spiral on the next page.

How is the pattern of your spiral similar to the concentric circles that you made?

Look around you. Find at least two concentric circles and two spirals in your world.

CIRCLES	SPIRALS
1.	1.
2.	2.
3.	3.
4.	4.
5.	5.

Circles and Spirals

Fill in this chart showing the temperature readings for 12 hours.

HOUR	1	2	3	4	5	6
TEMP						
HOUR	7	8	9	10	11	12
TEMP						

Graph these temperature changes below.

Temperature

Hour of the Day

MATHEMATICS

Temperature

Record the daily temperature and weather conditions on the chart. Record this data for a number of weeks. Make your observations at the same time each day.

	Sunday	Monday	Tuesday	Wednesday	Thursday	Friday	Saturday
First Week							
Second Week							
Third Week							
Fourth Week							
Fifth Week							

Compare weather conditions and temperature readings for:

MONDAYS

WEDNESDAYS

FRIDAYS

_____ (any other day of your choice)

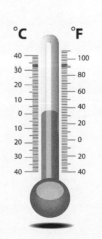

Can You Find It?

Search in your environment for this shape:

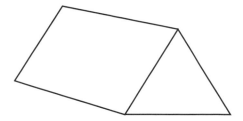

List the different places you find the shape in some form.

1.

2.

3.

4.

5.

6.

7.

8.

9.

10.

In your opinion, is this a strong supportive structure?
Explain your answer.

Number Pattern Designs

Create a numeric design using the following numbers:

   3, 4, 5, 6, 7, 8, 9, 10, 11

The sums must be the same in all directions.

Now create other geometric arrangements. Use other operations of mathematics if you can.

Your Heart Rate

Measure your pulse after doing the following activities. Relax for about five minutes after each activity before counting your heart rate. Record your data on the line graph below.

Heart Rate

_____ When first beginning activity

_____ Jog in place one minute

_____ After five-minute rest

_____ Do 15 jumping jacks

_____ After five-minute rest

Heart Rate

_____ Touch your toes 10 times

_____ After five-minute rest

_____ Touch your toes 15 times

_____ After five-minute rest

Activity and Rest Period

Number of Counts

Which activity resulted in the highest pulse count?

After each five-minute rest, was your heart rate exactly the same?

Why do you think this may be true?

Polygons

Make various closed polygons in the space below. The perimeter of each shape must equal 3" (inches). Label each polygon with the number of sides. How many different shapes did you make? _____

Which shape had the longest side? _____

Compare the longest side of each shape.

Polygons

Draw squares with different side measurements. After drawing the squares, measure and label the perimeters of each.

Polygons

Refer to the squares you made on page 86.
Create a graph to show length of side versus perimeter.

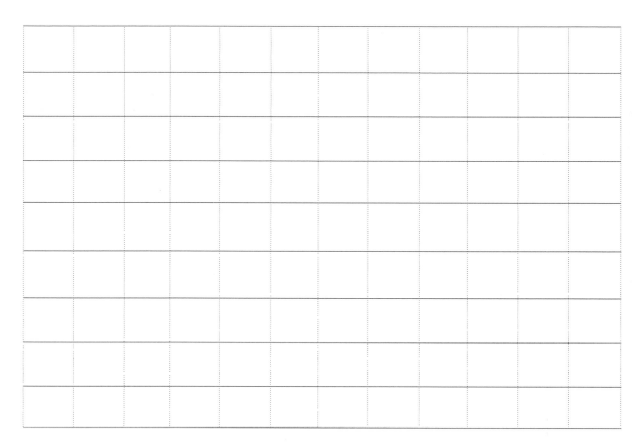

Length of One Side

Perimeter

Can you draw any conclusions about your results? List your ideas.

1.

2.

3.

4.

5.

6.

7.

Polygons

Determine the areas of the squares you made. Make another graph showing the length of the perimeters of each square and the area of each of the squares.

Length of Perimeter

Area of Each Square

Analyze the data on your graph. What conclusions can you draw about perimeters and areas of squares?

Sides, Faces, Vertices and Edges

Draw shapes with 3 sides, 5 sides, 7 sides and 8 sides on the next page. Use a ruler to create these shapes.

Make a chart to compare the number of sides and number of vertices.

	SIDES	VERTICES
3		
5		
7		
8		

What conclusions can you draw?

Will this conclusion be true for any number of sides?

What relationship can you discover among the number of faces, edges, and vertices?

Use models of the following solids to complete the chart below.

1) cube   4) cone

2) triangular prism   5) sphere

3) cylinder   6) square-based pyramid

	# Vertices	# Edges	# Faces
CUBE			
TRIANGULAR PRISM			
CYLINDER			
CONE			
SPHERE			
PYRAMID			

Shapes

Family Tree

Research your family.
Design a chart on the next page and fill in names of your relatives.
Include birth and death dates.
1. Compute life spans.
2. Note first and middle names.

What conclusions can you make?

Relatives

What would each of these relatives be to you?

Mother's sister _____

Sister's brother _____

Father's wife's mother _____

Father's brother _____

Father's brother's son _____

Grandmother's son's daughter _____

Father's wife's brother _____

Mother's husband's sister _____

Father's father _____

Brother's uncle's son _____

Sister's uncle's wife _____

Sister's husband's son _____

Make up some of your own.
1.
2.
3.
4.
5.

Family Tree

Differentiate between tiny and small. Give examples of each.

Order these "little" words from least to greatest in the left column.

MICROSCOPIC   PIGMY   SLIGHT   MINISCULE   WEE   LITTLE
DWARFISH   TINY   MEAN   MINIATURE   SMALL   PETITE   MINUTE

       "LITTLE" WORD   OBJECT AS EXAMPLE

1.

2.

3.

4.

5.

6.

7.

8.

9.

10.

11.

12.

13.

Identify an object, living or non-living, to fit your "little" order. Write your ideas on the list above.

Little

How would your point of view change of what was "little" if you were the height of a mouse? List several differences.

1.
2.
3.
4.
5.
6.
7.

Draw a picture showing you the size of a mouse and the world around you.

Big

Here are words describing "quantity."

BIG	HUGE	ENORMOUS	GRAND	TITANIC	MONSTROUS
AMPLE	MASSIVE	CORPULENT	COPIOUS	BULKY	PLENTIFUL

List more words you know or can find to describe "big."

1.   5.

2.   6.

3.   7.

4.   8.

Order the objects below, relying on your understanding of size.

CAR   BICYCLE   NEWSPAPER   SNOWPLOW   LOCOMOTIVE   ENGINE
ICEBERG   MOON   ELM TREE   JUPITER   SUBMARINE   SKYSCRAPER
REDWOOD   PLUTO

1.   8.

2.   9.

3.   10.

4.   11.

5.   12.

6.   13.

7.   14.

Was this difficult for you? Explain why or why not.

Big

How would your life change if you grew to a height of 8 feet while sleeping tonight? List as many changes as you can imagine.

1.

2.

3.

4.

5.

6.

7.

8.

9.

10.

11.

12.

13.

14.

15.

16.

17.

18.

19.

20.

Order

Number this drawing to indicate the steps in folding a flat sheet of paper into a CUBE.

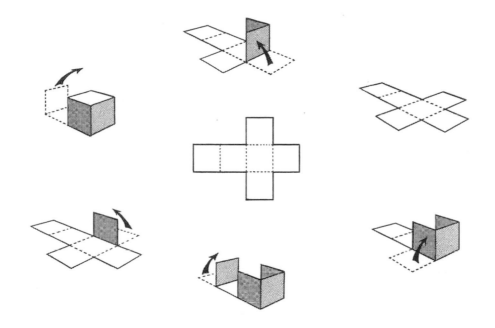

Number this drawing to show the steps for creating a PYRAMID.

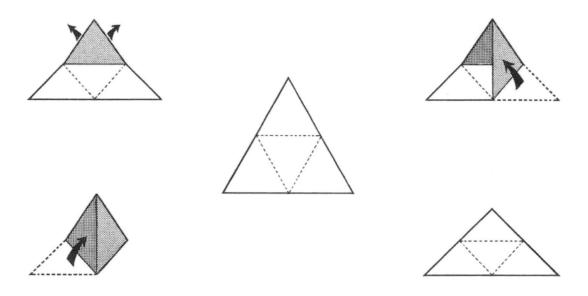

Symmetry

Fold a piece of paper and cut out a shape that begins and ends on the fold. Open your shape. This shape is symmetrical because it is the same on both sides. Which of these shapes are symmetrical? Color each symmetrical shape.

What is asymmetrical? Draw some figures that are asymmetrical.

Name things in your world that are symmetrical.

1.
2.
3.
4.
5.

6.
7.
8.
9.
10.

Are you symmetrical? Why or why not?

Perspective Drawing – One Point

Here is an example of one-point perspective drawing.

1. Begin with a shape and a point.

2. Extend lines. From the corners of the shape to meet at the point.

3. Draw lines parallel to the original shape.

4. Erase the unnecessary lines.

Draw each of these shapes in perspective.

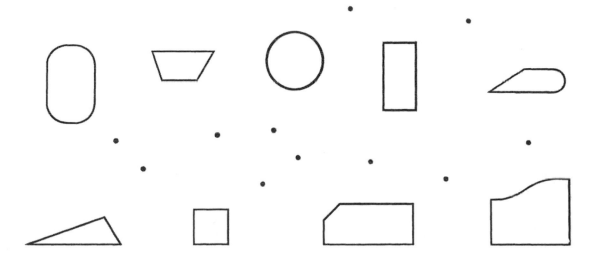

Make a drawing of your own using one-point perspective.

Tangrams

History tells us that the Tangram Puzzle was invented in China over 4000 years ago. People have made many designs and pictures using the shapes of the tangram.

Try to make these designs by fitting together the tangram pieces from page 101.

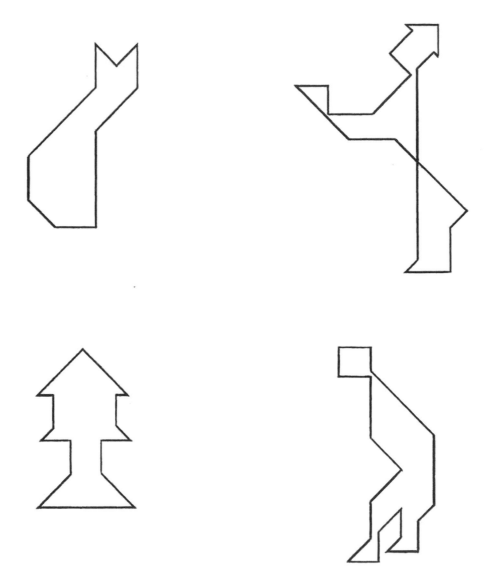

On the following pages, make your own tangram puzzles or figures. Trace around your designs. Decorate your figures. Ask a friend to try to make your designs.

Tangrams

Cut out each part of the tangram very carefully.

Trace each shape on card stock or index cards to be used as patterns.

Cut out your patterns.

Try to form a large square using all of these pieces.

Tangrams

My Own Tangram Puzzles

My Own Tangram Puzzles

Flow Charts

A flow chart is a step-by-step way to do something.
Study this example: HOW TO KNOCK ON A DOOR

STEPS

1. Walk up to the door

2. Raise hand

3. Make fist

4. Hit door three times

5. Wait

6. Does anyone answer?

    Yes – go to step 7
    No – go to step 4

7. Say "hello"

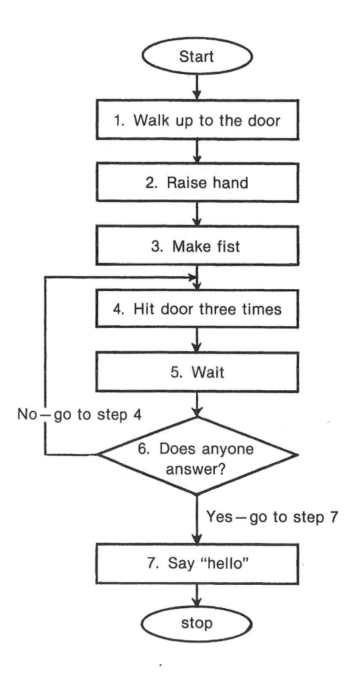

Flow Charts

These are flow chart symbols:

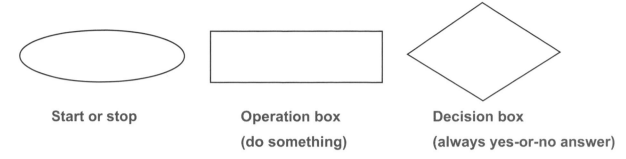

Start or stop	**Operation box** **(do something)**	**Decision box** **(always yes-or-no answer)**

Directions:

(Do tasks A-D on a separate sheet of paper.)

A. Design a flow chart for any of the problems listed below.
1. How to polish a car.
2. How to brush your teeth.
3. How to set the dining room table.
4. How to put on shoes and socks.
5. How to take a bath.

B. List the steps for the problem that you have selected.

C. Use appropriate flow chart shapes and arrows to show your steps.

D. Choose one of these mathematical problems and construct a set of steps and a flow chart.
1. How to average your grades.
2. How to tell if a number is odd or even.
3. How to measure the distance around a circle.
4. How to find the perimeter of a square.

E. Write a mathematical "how to" problem of your own.

Flow Charts

Stock Exchange

Choose one stock from the financial section of the newspaper (New York Stock Exchange or American Stock Exchange).

Imagine that you have $1,000 to invest in this stock.

Name your stock and set up a graph for 30 days. Record the closing prices quoted each day in the newspaper and plot the changes. Prices are usually quoted by Va point changes. It is a wise idea to place the first closing price in the middle of the price column to allow for upward and downward price changes.

Price

Date
(No Saturdays or Sundays – The Stock
Exchange is closed on weekends.)

If you invested $1,000 at the closing price on the first day, did you make or lose money by the last day? _____ How much? _____

List similarities among all United States coins.

1.
2.
3.
4.
5.
6.
7.
8.
9.
10.

Design a new United States coin. Draw both sides of your coin. Clearly show dates, lettering, figures and other important features.

Name the American personality you will put on your coin. Tell why you chose this person.

How will the design of your coin be different than current U.S. coins? What material will you use to make your coin?

Questions of My Own

As you are thinking, you may design a deep thought question of your own. Record the lesson you were working on and the date of your work. Write each question clearly and neatly.

Lesson #   Date   My Questions

_____   _____   _____

_____   _____   _____

_____   _____   _____

_____   _____   _____

_____   _____   _____

_____   _____   _____

_____   _____   _____

_____   _____   _____

_____   _____   _____

_____   _____   _____

_____   _____   _____

_____   _____   _____

SCIENCE: LIVING THINGS

Activities	Date Begun	Teacher's Initials
1. Animal Locomotion		
2. Animal Food-Getting		
3. Adaptations		
4. Like Produces Like		
5. Hybrids		
6. Life Spans		
7. Endangered Species		
8. Whales		
9. Bats		
10. Metamorphosis		
11. Insect Sounds		
12. Social Habits		
13. Moths and Butterflies		
14. Seed Germination		
15. Redwood Trees		
16. Cork		
17. Dinosaurs		
18. A New Find!		
QUESTIONS OF MY OWN		

Animal Locomotion

Animal locomotion is related to the habits of food-getting, reproduction, and protection. In higher animals, locomotion is exhibited as flying, running, crawling, swimming, and hopping.

In an imaginary race, which of these mammals would be the fastest? Circle your answer.

Cheetah   Bear   Human   Dog

Explain your answer. Describe the body structure of each of these animals and relate the structure to the animals' finishing position.

For each animal below, explain the relationship between the animal's body structure and its method of locomotion.

DEER

TURTLE

PELICAN

GOLDEN EAGLE

The bones of all flying birds are hollow, unlike those of a human being. Of what value are hollow bones?

Study about birds that cannot fly. Explain why these birds have lost their ability to fly.

Animal Food-Getting

The primary source of all energy for animals is the food manufactured by green plants during the process of photosynthesis.

Define these words:

HERBIVORE
OMNIVORE
CARNIVORE

Classify the following animals by their eating habits.

Tyrannosaurus rex	mouse	owl
robin	sparrow	lion
hamster	raccoon	penguin
giraffe	sheep	deer
human	Apatosaurus	elephant

HERBIVORE	**CARNIVORE**	**OMNIVORE**

Adaptations

Many animals have structural or behavioral adaptations that protect them from animal predators. Some of these adaptations are related to seasons of the year, or are automatic and unlearned.

List animals with protective coloration, also known as camouflage.

1.

2.

3.

4.

5.

6.

7.

8.

9.

10.

List protective changes in animals' behavior.

Compare or contrast color changes with natural protective coloration.

Like Produces Like

Explain how puppies are like adult dogs.

In what ways are human young like human adults?

How are children different from adults?

List things the adults of a species might do for their young.

How is "young-care" similar for dogs and human beings?

Hybrids

A hybrid is the offspring of two different species. For example, a mule is the result of a horse and a donkey mating, and the beefalo is the offspring of a cow and a buffalo.

Make up a new name for the resulting hybrid offspring if these pairs of animals would mate.

DEER and ANTELOPE

SEAGULL and PIGEON

FLY and HONEY BEE

CHIPMUNK and MOUSE

MOLE and RAT

PORCUPINE and ANTEATER

Make up word combinations of your own for other offspring.

Choose one of those names and draw a picture of the new species.

Life Spans

Record the "growing up" period and life span of each animal.

	GROWING UP	LIFE SPAN
robin		
dog		
elephant		
turtle		
chicken		
human		
giraffe		
salmon		
cat		
chimpanzee		

Compare the lengths of time (growing up vs. life span).
What conclusions can you draw from your findings?

Endangered Species

Show the migration path of seals.

Describe their eating habits.

These animals are in danger of becoming extinct. Suggest ways humans can help these animals to continue to flourish.

Endangered Species

Read about other endangered species. List animals in danger of becoming extinct and the country and habitat of each.

ANIMAL   COUNTRY AND HABITAT

Can you draw any conclusions about the animals, their homes and habitats by comparing what you have learned?

Overall, what is the greatest enemy of each species?

Whales

How are whales like dogs?

How are whales like fish?

It has been said that killer whales are very intelligent. What advantages can you see to an intelligent animal living under water instead of living on land as humans do?

Bats

Read stories and fables about bats.

In your opinion, how are bats like birds? Consider size, body parts, eating habits, and sleeping habits.

How are bats like mice?

Are bats warm-blooded or cold-blooded animals?

In your opinion, what would be the advantages and disadvantages of being a bat?

Metamorphosis

Construct a chart showing the stages of metamorphosis.

Give an illustration for each stage below.

Look up the passage in *Alice's Adventures in Wonderland* in which Alice has a conversation with the caterpillar about metamorphosis. Relate his explanation to your chart.

Insect Sounds

List insects that make sounds that are audible to human beings.

Explain how each insect make its sound.

1.

2.

3.

4.

5.

6.

7.

**Compare and contrast insect sounds to the sounds of mammals
Consider body parts and structure in your explanation.**

Social Habits

Read all you can about ants and bees.

Describe the society for each insect. Include the specific task each member of the society performs.

ANTS   BEES

List similarities between the societal structure of ants or bees to the societal structure of human beings.

1.

2.

3.

4.

5.

6.

7.

8.

9.

10.

Moths and Butterflies

DID YOU KNOW?

1. **Butterflies have antennae with knobs.**
   Moths have feathery antennae.

2. **Butterflies fly during the day.**
   Moths fly at night.

3. **Butterflies land with wings in a V.**
   Moths land with flattened wings.

Investigate the statements listed above.

How do these specific differences equip the insects for life?

If a butterfly and moth could mate and produce a hybrid, what insect might result? Invent a name for this offspring.

Draw and label the body parts of this "new" insect. Label specific parts and color the insect.

Seed Germination

Considering the conditions necessary for germination, explain each step of the germination process.

Draw illustrations of a legume through its germination process.

Redwood Trees

Read all you can about Redwood trees (Sequoia semperviens).

How old are the Redwood trees?

How is it possible for scientists to determine the age of trees without cutting them down?

Explain why Redwood trees have been able to survive for so many years.

How do forest plants compete with one another?

Explain how it is possible for water from the soil to rise to the very top of such tall trees.

Make a time line on the next page equal to the life span of a typical Redwood tree. List some important historical happenings during the same period of time. Use book or Internet resources to help you.

Redwood Time Line

_____

_____

_____

_____

_____

_____

_____

_____

_____

_____

_____

_____

Cork

Where does cork come from?

Describe its properties.

Invent some new ways to use cork.

Illustrate one of these new uses.

Dinosaurs

Read all you can about prehistoric animals.

Make a chart to show the three periods during which dinosaurs lived and list some of the dinosaurs of each period.

_____   _____   _____

Review data the scientists have used to hypothesize why dinosaurs became extinct. In your opinion, which speculation seems most likely to be true? Explain your thinking.

On the next page, draw the "Land of Dinosaurs." Include plant and animal life, mountains and land forms, and water. Color your drawing and label each animal.

"The Land of Dinosaurs"

A New Find!

These skeletal parts were discovered in the Siberian Desert. Using the shapes of the body parts, make a drawing of the assembled skeleton.

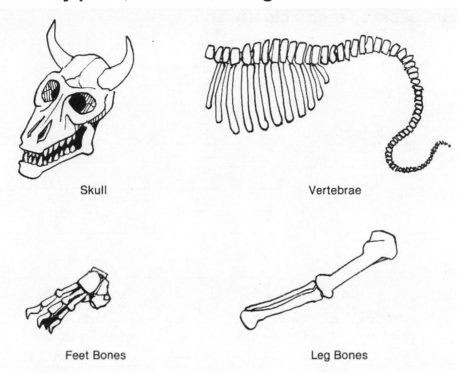

Skull

Vertebrae

Feet Bones

Leg Bones

Using the knowledge you have learned about other dinosaurs, describe how this animal must have lived, what he ate, and in what period he must have existed.

Questions of My Own

As you are thinking, you may design a deep thought question of your own. Record the lesson you were working on and the date of your work. Write each question clearly and neatly.

Lesson #   Date   My Questions

_____   _____   _____

_____   _____   _____

_____   _____   _____

_____   _____   _____

_____   _____   _____

_____   _____   _____

_____   _____   _____

_____   _____   _____

_____   _____   _____

_____   _____   _____

_____   _____   _____

_____   _____   _____

_____   _____   _____

SCIENCE: THE EARTH AND BEYOND

Activities	Date Begun	Teacher's Initials
1. Earth's Composition		
2. Improve the Planet Earth		
3. Topography		
4. Pollution of Water		
5. Pollution of Air		
6. Volcanoes		
7. Rainbows		
8. Hurricanes		
9. Tornadoes		
10. Hail		
11. Clouds		
12. Lightning		
13. Sound		
14. Light		
15. Rocks		
16. Try This Experiment		
17. Fire		
18. The Moon and Satellites		
19. An Eclipse		
20. Constellations		
QUESTIONS OF MY OWN		

Earth's Composition

The earth is composed of three main parts: lithosphere, hydrosphere, and atmosphere. Define each word.

LITHOSPHERE

HYDROSPHERE

ATMOSPHERE

Categorize each of the words listed below.

Atlantic Ocean	Spain
London	Mediterranean Sea
Wind Currents	Siberian Desert
Grand Canyon	Antarctica
Mississippi River	Persian Gulf
Alaska	Clouds
Saudi Arabia	Istanbul
Caribbean Sea	Red Sea
Mexico	Aurora Borealis

LITHOSPHERE　　　**HYDROSPHERE**　　　**ATMOSPHERE**

Improve the Planet Earth

Consider the land forms, weather, animal and plant life, mineral supplies, and human inhabitants. List or illustrate your improvement ideas for our planet.

Predict how the improvements may affect the planet in 100 years.

Compose a limerick or song to include in a commercial to "sell" your ideas for improvements.

Topography

Read about forces that cause changes in the earth's surface. What forces cause changes in the earth's surface to take place rapidly?

What changes take place slowly?

In your opinion, which occurrence has the greatest affect on the earth's surface? Explain your answer.

Pollution of Water

Water is sometimes called the "universal solvent." How do you think this characteristic of water may be related to the water pollution problem?

Thermal Pollution

Why might dumping hot water into rivers and streams be a pollutant?

Suggest ways to avoid this problem.

Illustrate what happens to the plant and animal life in a pond when thermal pollution occurs.

Pollution Prevention

Many communities have laws forbidding the burning of trash and leaves. What other laws are needed to prevent pollution of air, pollution of land, and pollution of water?

AIR LAWS

LAND LAWS

WATER LAWS

Volcanoes

Learn about the ancient town of Pompeii. Find Pompeii on a map. Relate its location to the volcano belts of the world.

Read about a seismograph. How does it measure the activity of volcanoes?

Draw and label a cross-section of a volcano.

Construct a model of a volcano from plaster of Paris or papier-mâché. Use baking soda and vinegar to demonstrate a volcanic eruption. Describe your demonstration below.

Volcano's Name:

Rainbows

Read all you can about rainbows.
Explain why rainbows form.

Why are rainbows curved or semi-circular?

Name the colors of a rainbow.

Are the colors of the rainbow always in the same order? Explain.

Reflect means "to bounce back."
Name some materials that reflect light well.

1.   6.

2.   7.

3.   8.

4.   9.

5.   10.

Hurricanes

Read about "hurricane hunters." Hurricane hunters are pilots who fly into the eye of a storm to locate its center and track its direction.

In your opinion, why would a person consider doing a job like this?

Would you consider training for this job? Why or why not?

Tornadoes

Tornadoes usually form in late spring over dark farmland. How do you think the color of the dark, moist soil may be related to the formation of a tornado? List four conditions that are usually present when a tornado forms.

Make a drawing to show and explain qualities of a tornado.

Hail

Read about and describe the conditions usually present when hail forms.

In your opinion, is hail a helpful or harmful weather phenomenon? List your ideas.

HELPFUL   HARMFUL

We understand how and why hailstones form. In ancient times, people believed that the gods caused various happenings in nature according to their feelings about man. How did early humans explain hail? Make up a possible explanation that may have been offered.

Clouds

Read about clouds.
Draw and label pictures of each kind of cloud you have read about.

Listen to the weather report each morning for a week. Record the daily prediction on the chart below. At the same time, observe the daytime skies. Record the kinds of clouds that you see.

	WEATHER PREDICTION	KIND OF CLOUDS
Day 1		
Day 2		
Day 3		
Day 4		
Day 5		
Day 6		
Day 7		

Based on your chart above, do you feel that clouds are useful predictors of weather? Why or why not?

Lightning

Lightning is sometimes called "energy out of control."
Is this a good description? Explain your reasoning.

Suppose a bad storm knocked out the electric power in your home.
Name other sources of light your family might use.

Is "giant spark" a good name for lightning? Who may have made up this name? Why?

Read about Benjamin Franklin's experiment with the kite that proved that lightning is electricity. What is a lightning rod? How does it help?

Sound

All sounds are produced by vibrating objects. Humans can hear only those sounds produced by vibration of between 20 and 20,000 cycles per second (CPS). Newer nomenclature for CPS is Hertz, named for Heinrich Hertz, a pioneer physicist.

Rapid vibrations produce high sound. Read about the term decibel. Is sound a form of matter or energy? Explain your thinking.

Tuning Fork

Borrow a tuning fork. Tap the fork and listen to the sound. Place it against wood, metal, glass, the floor, a glass of water, etc. What happens? How or why does it work?

The closer together particles of matter are, the better sound is transmitted. What do you think would happen if an astronaut used a tuning fork on the moon?

Light

Define these words:

TRANSPARENT

TRANSLUCENT

OPAQUE

Name materials through which light cannot pass.

1.   6.

2.   7.

3.   8.

4.   9.

5.   10.

How are shadows created?

Try this experiment. Use two objects of different heights. Measure their shadows at different times on a sunny day. Graph the length of the object and its shadow at these hours. Compare the graphs. What conclusions can you make?

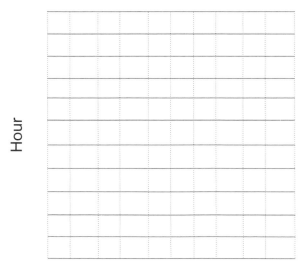

Length of Shadow

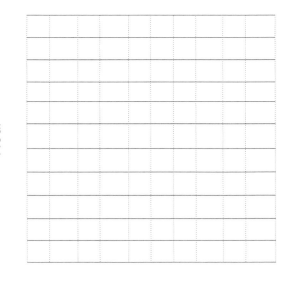

Length of Shadow

Rocks

Define the three main kinds of rock:

    IGNEOUS

    SEDIMENTARY

    METAMORPHIC

Explain the differences between each kind.

Explain how each is affected by the following:

WATER

1.

2.

3.

WIND

1.

2.

3.

COLD

1.

2.

3.

HEAT

1.

2.

3.

Try This Experiment

Place about two handfuls of sand, pebbles, stone and plant pieces in a heavy glass jar. Fill the jar with water and cover securely. Slowly and carefully turn the jar over several times. Observe what occurs. Record your observations below.

Make a connection between your observations and the possible carrying power of water in the settling process of materials in rivers and streams. Explain your thinking.

Fire

Name the three conditions necessary to create fire or combustion.

    1.

    2.

    3.

Place a jar over a lighted candle with adult supervision.
Record your observations.

List ways fire is helpful to humans.

    1.

    2.

    3.

    4.

    5.

List ways fires are harmful to man.

    1.

    2.

    3.

    4.

    5.

The Moon and Satellites

Have you ever heard people talk about the "man in the moon" or say that the moon is made of "green cheese"? How do you think these ideas got started?

Read about the craters of the moon.
List some of their names.

The moon is called the earth's "natural satellite." Tiros, Telstar, and others are called "man-made satellites." Read about man-made satellites. In what way is the moon similar to a man-made satellite?

An Eclipse

Read all you can about solar eclipses.
Draw a series of pictures below to show the stages of an eclipse.

Find the dates of future eclipses in a reference book or
on the Internet. Record dates below.

How do astronomers predict the future dates of eclipses?

What is the difference between a solar eclipse and a lunar eclipse?

Constellations

Star constellations were named by early men who thought they could really see figures in the heavens. Study an illustration of winter skies in the northern hemisphere and find a new being or animal. Draw the figure, using key stars. Name your constellation. Write a story about your character on another sheet of paper.

Create more constellations with other stars. Draw them below.

Questions of My Own

As you are thinking, you may design a deep thought question of your own. Record the lesson you were working on and the date of your work. Write each question clearly and neatly.

Lesson #   Date   My Questions

SCIENCE: MACHINES, IDEAS AND INVENTIONS

Activities	Date Begun	Teacher's Initials
1. Maps	_____	_____
2. Alaska	_____	_____
3. Can You Find It?	_____	_____
4. Discovery	_____	_____
5. Rockets	_____	_____
6. Model Oil Field	_____	_____
7. Wheels	_____	_____
8. Bridges	_____	_____
9. Automobiles	_____	_____
10. Kites	_____	_____
11. The Pulley	_____	_____
12. Vapor	_____	_____
13. Trains	_____	_____
14. Water Vessels	_____	_____

QUESTIONS OF MY OWN _____ _____

Maps

Use your map skills to develop a map of an imaginary place. Choose a "motif" (theme) that appeals to you.

Your map must include:

1. a name
2. a legend

3. compass rose
4. scale of miles

Some natural features to consider are: forests, caves, deserts, oceans, mountain ranges, valleys, canyons, rivers, lakes, etc. Man-made features may be cities, roads, schools, hospitals, and bridges.

Alaska

Find Alaska on a map. Learn all you can about the climate and how the natives' lives are affected by the weather.

Describe how the climate and people of Alaska would be different if the temperature were always 40° warmer during each season.

Can You Find It?

Where would this island be located?

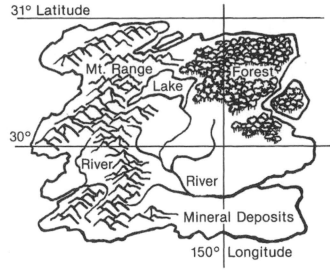

Describe the climate you might expect to find.

You are a leader of settlers.
Where will you suggest your followers make their homes?

What reasons will you use to convince your settlers that your choice is best?

1.

2.

3.

4.

5.

Once your settlers make their decision, what are the first activities you must all do? List them.

1.

2.

3.

4.

5.

Discovery

Imagine that you have accidentally discovered an uncharted island. While exploring, you meet the primitive natives that have lived here for thousands of years.

List inventions or discovery ideas these people would not have.

After reporting your discovery to the scientists and government, you are assigned to prepare these primitive natives for the "outside, modern world."

In order of importance, record the activities or learnings that would have to be accomplished for or by these people.

Suggest ways to accomplish the modernization you suggest.

Rockets

There are three scientific principles that apply to rockets. They are called Newton's Laws of Motion, named after Sir Isaac Newton, a famous English scientist.

Newton's First Law: Objects at rest stay at rest; objects in motion stay in motion in a straight line unless acted upon by some unbalanced force.

Newton's Second Law: Force equals mass times acceleration ($F = ma$).

Newton's Third Law: For every action there must be an equal and opposite reaction.

Put together all three of Newton's Laws of Motion to describe the launch of a rocket.

Model Oil Field

Construct a model oil field. Use wood for the oil layer and show a cut-away section of the various layers of earth under the well.

Label all parts and attach an explanation of how your well operates.

Sketch your model below before you begin to build.

Wheels

Do research about the history of the wheel and its development.

How would life be different today if there were no wheels?

Design a vehicle to carry at least one person without using the invention of the wheel.

Bridges

Draw illustrations of different kinds of bridges.

Why are there different kinds of bridges?

In your opinion, is one bridge better than another?
Explain your answer.

Automobiles

Read all you can about automobiles (cars) of the past. From your reading or observations you have made while visiting museums, make a list of improvements made to automobiles over time.

1.

2.

3.

4.

5.

In your judgment, which improvement was the best? Rewrite your list in order of greatest value to the modernization of the first car.

1.

2.

3.

4.

5.

If you could further improve the automobile, what single improvement would you suggest? Explain your idea.

Design a car to increase speed and also conserve energy. Draw your design on the next page. Consider these areas:

1. Type of energy to be used
2. Purpose of your model
3. Type of material used in construction
4. Construction procedures
5. Cost

My Car

Read all you can about Chinese kites.

In your own words, explain how a kite flies.

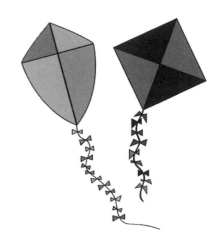

Design a kite of your own. Describe the materials you would use to build it. Decorate your kite and give it a name. Keep in mind all that you have learned about aerodynamics.

Pulleys

Read all about pulleys and how they work.

Design a pulley system and illustrate it below. Include materials and measurements for your project. Suggest the specific work your pulley may do.

Using your diagram, can you construct your pulley?
Make a model using your ideas.

Vapor

Explain why people breathe out "dragon smoke" on cold days.

Do frogs ever breathe out "dragon smoke"? Why or why not?

Why does a tea kettle whistle?

Trains

Read about the trains of the past. Some interesting aspects are the stories of laying railroad tracks across the United States, famous locomotive rides, development of power sources, and hobos.

Retell the story of JOHN HENRY in your own words.

Describe and illustrate how a steam engine works.

Trains

If you could travel like a hobo for a month, where would you go and what would you expect to see?

1.

2.

3.

4.

5.

6.

7.

8.

9.

10.

What are some of the problems you may face during this month as a hobo?

1.

2.

3.

4.

5.

6.

7.

8.

9.

10.

Trains

Read all you can about High Speed Tube Transportation. There are certain dangers involved in this manner of transportation. List safety precautions you feel are necessary to prevent accidents.

1.

2.

3.

4.

5.

6.

7.

8.

Of all the methods of transportation, in your opinion, which method is safest? Explain your answer.

Which methods of transportation seem most dangerous? Why?

Water Vessels

Learn all you can about water vessels of the past. Try to read about lost treasures, pirates, war ships, luxury passenger vessels, and submarines.

List some differences in characteristics or manner in the pirates you read about.

What makes a "good" pirate good?

What makes a "bad" pirate bad?

Draw a ship that indicates size, home country, and crew for you and your pirate crew.

Water Vessels

Explain and illustrate what is meant by an outboard motor.

List some rules of safety for leisure water craft.

Underwater Vessels

Draw a cross-section of an underwater vessel on the next page. Include a control room, power source, living quarters, kitchen, laundry, recreational or leisure facilities, refuse area, etc., that would be needed for an underwater voyage lasting at least six months.

Underwater Vessel

Questions of My Own

As you are thinking, you may design a deep thought question of your own. Record the lesson you were working on and the date of your work. Write each question clearly and neatly.

Lesson #   Date   My Questions

Dynamic Workshops!

Nathan Levy is a dynamic speaker who has presented teacher, parent, and student workshops from New York to China on a wide array of topics. Nathan is a veteran educator who has taught in urban, rural, and suburban schools. He shares ways to effectively improve teaching and learning in the classroom and at home. In his role as school principal, Mr. Levy has modeled instructional leadership in an exemplary manner. Mr. Levy is the author of the famous logic series *Stories with Holes* as well as several other educational books. All of Mr. Levy's books promote higher order thinking.

The various topics for workshops which Mr. Levy presents are of great benefit to educators as well as parents. The topics focus on such areas as:

Critical Thinking	Reading
Creativity	Writing
Parental Involvement	Science
Principal Training	Differentiating Instruction
Meeting the Standards	Teaching Gifted Children (in and out of the regular classroom)

Please contact us for more information about our workshops.

Nathan Levy Books LLC

18 Moorland Blvd
Monroe Twp NJ 08831

Phone 732-605-1643   **Fax 732-656-7822**

www.storieswithholes.com

NATHAN LEVY'S STORIES WITH HOLES
The famous logic stories that make kids think! Each book contains new stories for children ages 8-88 that stimulate divergent thinking skills. There are 20 volumes available.

WHOSE CLUES? by **NATHAN LEVY**
This 6 volume series of entertaining biographical quizzes keep children well-acquainted with famous people. Involves guessing and logical thinking.

NATHAN LEVY'S 100 INTRIGUING QUESTIONS
Each book in this 6 volume series stimulates critical thinking while improving creativity, speaking, and discussion skills.

NATHAN LEVY'S TEST BOOKLET BASIC KNOWLEDGE FOR EVERY AMERICAN OVER 9 YEARS OLD
The perfect activity book to assure that students acquire basic knowledge.

NOT JUST SCHOOLWORK by **AMY BURKE AND NATHAN LEVY**
The most dynamic and critical thinking book around. For grades 2 through 12.

WRITE FROM THE BEGINNING, by **AMY BURKE AND NATHAN LEVY**
Children in grades 1-5 have a lot to say about their world. The writing materials in this book break away from the same old assignments and forms, the result is highly-interested children with greater writing abilities.

Please contact us for more information or to place an order.

NATHAN LEVY BOOKS LLC

18 MOORLAND BLVD
MONROE TWP NJ 08831

PHONE 732-605-1643   **FAX 732-656-7822**

WWW.STORIESWITHHOLES.COM